REMEMBERING
LENT

*A Christian Devotional & Prayer Journal
for 40 Days of Bible Verses*

written & designed by Shalana Frisby

Get organized for success in your Bible study!
Download your bonus free printables now:

WWW.123JOURNALIT.COM / FREEBIES
SCRIPTURE FLASHCARDS – BIBLE READING PROMPTS – JOURNALING PAGES

More information at: www.123journalit.com

First Printing: February 2019
1 2 3 Journal It Publishing

ISBN-13: 978-1-947209-95-4

This journal belongs to

_____

start date :

_____

finish date :

_____

Bible verse reading list :

1. Mark 1:9-11
2. Mark 1:12-15
3. John 3:30-36
4. Psalm 42:1-4
5. Joel 1:14-16
6. Joel 2:12-14
7. Jonah 3:4-5 & 9-10
8. Matthew 6:16-18
9. Matthew 6:19-21
10. Isaiah 58:1-6
11. Isaiah 58:7-12
12. Colossians 3:12-15
13. Philippians 4:4-7
14. Matthew 4:1-4
15. Matthew 4:5-11
16. James 4:7-10
17. Psalm 139:17-18 & 23-24
18. 1 Peter 5:6-11
19. Daniel 9:3-6
20. 1 Corinthians 10:12-13

21. James 1:22-25
22. Job 23:8-12
23. John 10:6-10
24. Hebrews 12:1-3
25. Joshua 1:5-7
26. Philippians 3:7-11
27. Philippians 3:12-14
28. Matthew 5:13-16
29. Isaiah 43:25
30. John 13:33-35
31. 1 Timothy 3:14-16
32. John 16:31-33
33. John 17:1-5
34. John 17:13-19
35. Matthew 27:27-31
36. Matthew 27:45-51
37. Matthew 28:1-6
38. Matthew 28:7-10
39. Matthew 28:16-20
40. John 3:16-18

my additional scriptures :

_____   _____

_____   _____

_____   _____

BIBLE READING
write it out & study the verses

make note of today's scripture reference:

PRAYER REQUESTS
& praise for answered prayers

GIVE THANKS
what I am thankful for today

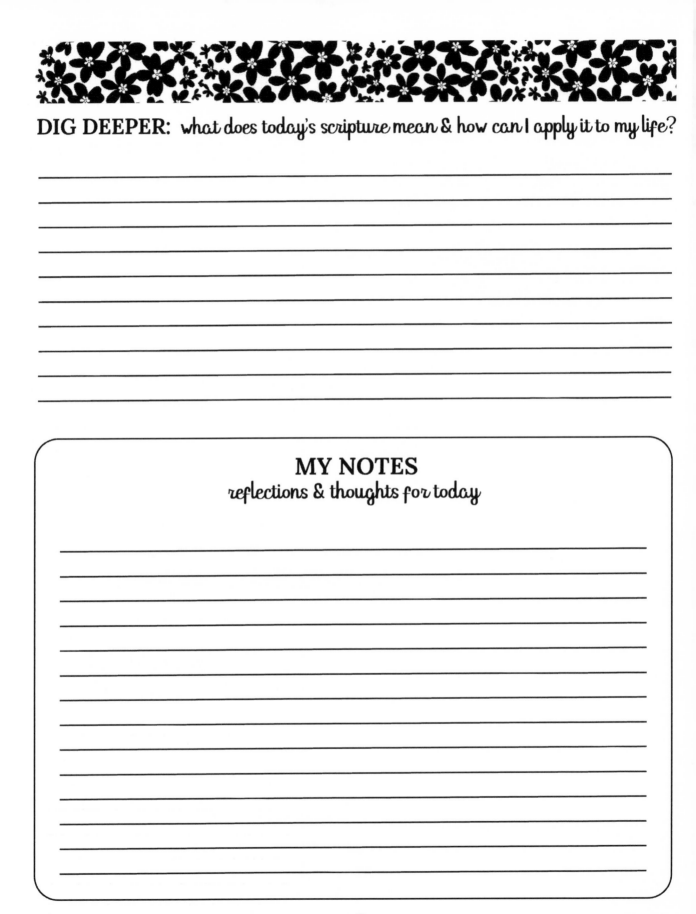

DIG DEEPER: *what does today's scripture mean & how can I apply it to my life?*

_____
_____
_____
_____
_____
_____
_____
_____
_____
_____

MY NOTES
reflections & thoughts for today

_____
_____
_____
_____
_____
_____
_____
_____
_____
_____
_____
_____

BIBLE READING
write it out & study the verses

make note of today's scripture reference:

PRAYER REQUESTS
& praise for answered prayers

GIVE THANKS
what I am thankful for today

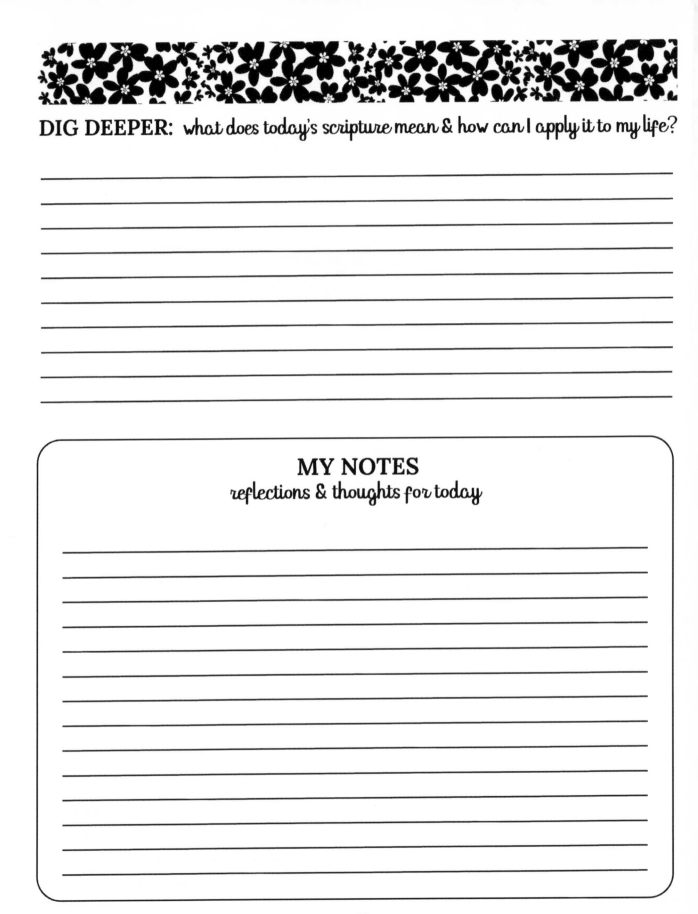

DIG DEEPER: *what does today's scripture mean & how can I apply it to my life?*

MY NOTES
reflections & thoughts for today

BIBLE READING
write it out & study the verses

make note of today's scripture reference:

PRAYER REQUESTS
& praise for answered prayers

GIVE THANKS
what I am thankful for today

DIG DEEPER: *what does today's scripture mean & how can I apply it to my life?*

_____
_____
_____
_____
_____
_____
_____
_____
_____
_____

MY NOTES
reflections & thoughts for today

_____
_____
_____
_____
_____
_____
_____
_____
_____
_____
_____
_____

BIBLE READING
write it out & study the verses

make note of today's scripture reference:

PRAYER REQUESTS
& praise for answered prayers

GIVE THANKS
what I am thankful for today

DIG DEEPER: what does today's scripture mean & how can I apply it to my life?

MY NOTES
reflections & thoughts for today

BIBLE READING
write it out & study the verses

make note of today's scripture reference:

PRAYER REQUESTS
& praise for answered prayers

GIVE THANKS
what I am thankful for today

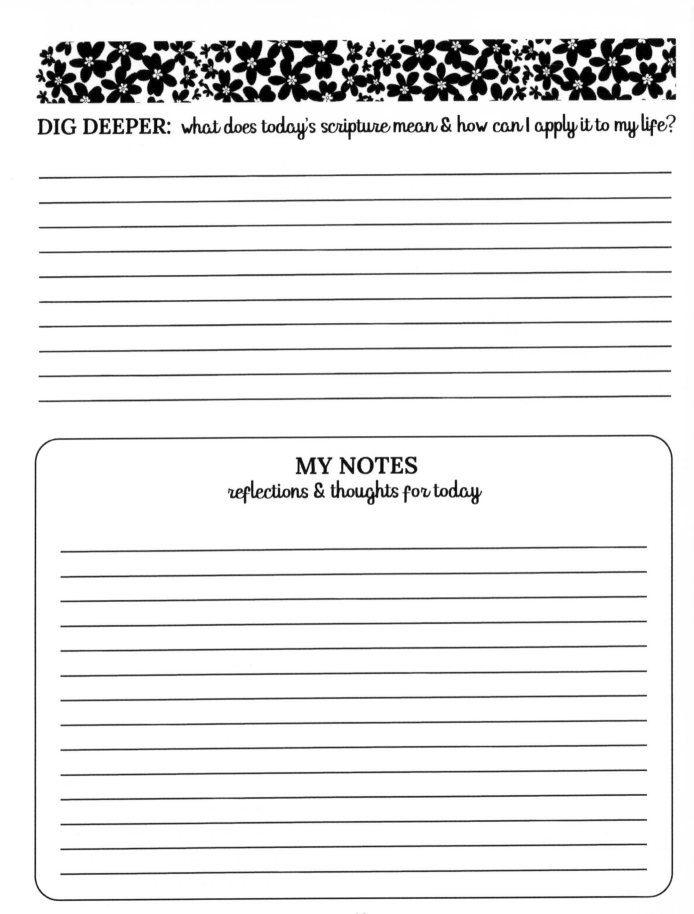

DIG DEEPER: what does today's scripture mean & how can I apply it to my life?

MY NOTES
reflections & thoughts for today

BIBLE READING
write it out & study the verses

make note of today's scripture reference:

PRAYER REQUESTS
& praise for answered prayers

GIVE THANKS
what I am thankful for today

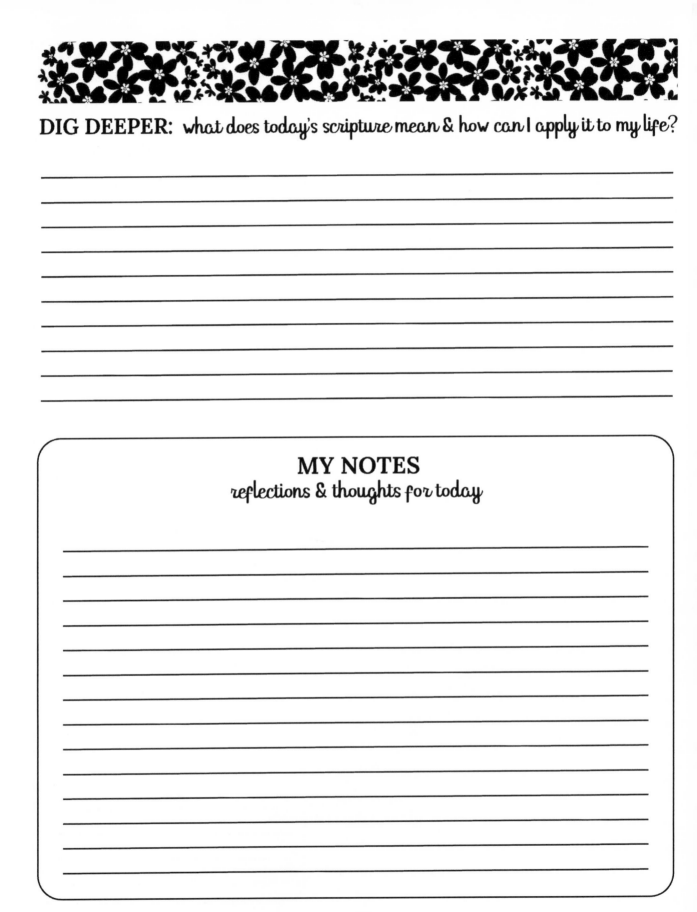

DIG DEEPER: *what does today's scripture mean & how can I apply it to my life?*

MY NOTES
reflections & thoughts for today

BIBLE READING
write it out & study the verses

make note of today's scripture reference:

PRAYER REQUESTS
& praise for answered prayers

GIVE THANKS
what I am thankful for today

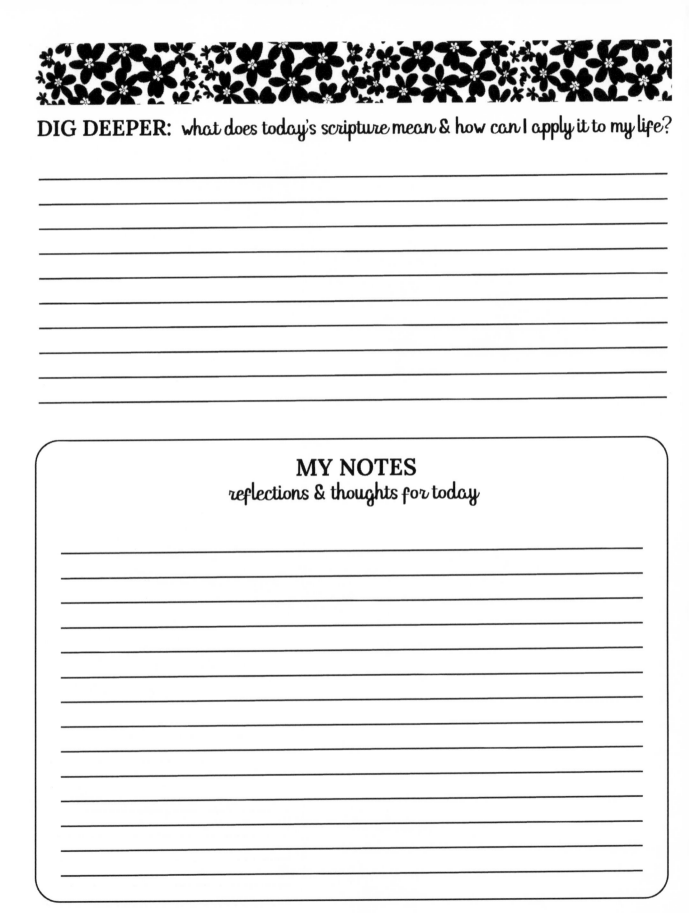

DIG DEEPER: *what does today's scripture mean & how can I apply it to my life?*

MY NOTES
reflections & thoughts for today

BIBLE READING
write it out & study the verses

make note of today's scripture reference:

PRAYER REQUESTS
& praise for answered prayers

GIVE THANKS
what I am thankful for today

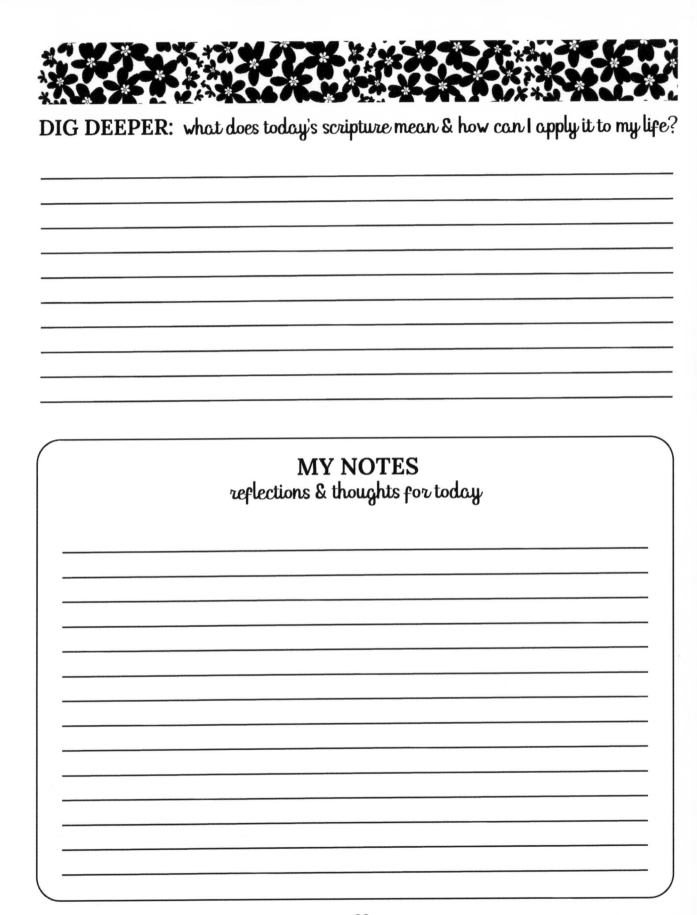

DIG DEEPER: what does today's scripture mean & how can I apply it to my life?

_____
_____
_____
_____
_____
_____
_____
_____
_____
_____
_____

MY NOTES
reflections & thoughts for today

_____
_____
_____
_____
_____
_____
_____
_____
_____
_____
_____
_____
_____
_____

BIBLE READING
write it out & study the verses

make note of today's scripture reference:

PRAYER REQUESTS
& praise for answered prayers

GIVE THANKS
what I am thankful for today

DIG DEEPER: *what does today's scripture mean & how can I apply it to my life?*

MY NOTES
reflections & thoughts for today

BIBLE READING
write it out & study the verses

make note of today's scripture reference:

PRAYER REQUESTS
& praise for answered prayers

GIVE THANKS
what I am thankful for today

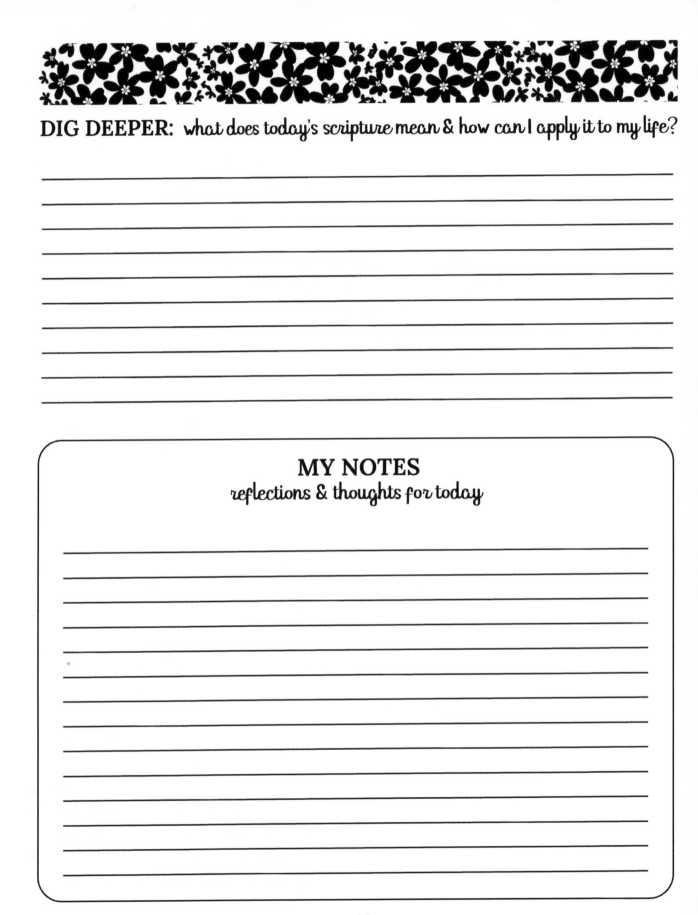

DIG DEEPER: what does today's scripture mean & how can I apply it to my life?

_____
_____
_____
_____
_____
_____
_____
_____
_____
_____

MY NOTES
reflections & thoughts for today

_____
_____
_____
_____
_____
_____
_____
_____
_____
_____
_____
_____
_____

BIBLE READING
write it out & study the verses

make note of today's scripture reference:

PRAYER REQUESTS
& praise for answered prayers

GIVE THANKS
what I am thankful for today

DIG DEEPER: *what does today's scripture mean & how can I apply it to my life?*

MY NOTES
reflections & thoughts for today

BIBLE READING
write it out & study the verses

make note of today's scripture reference:

PRAYER REQUESTS
& praise for answered prayers

GIVE THANKS
what I am thankful for today

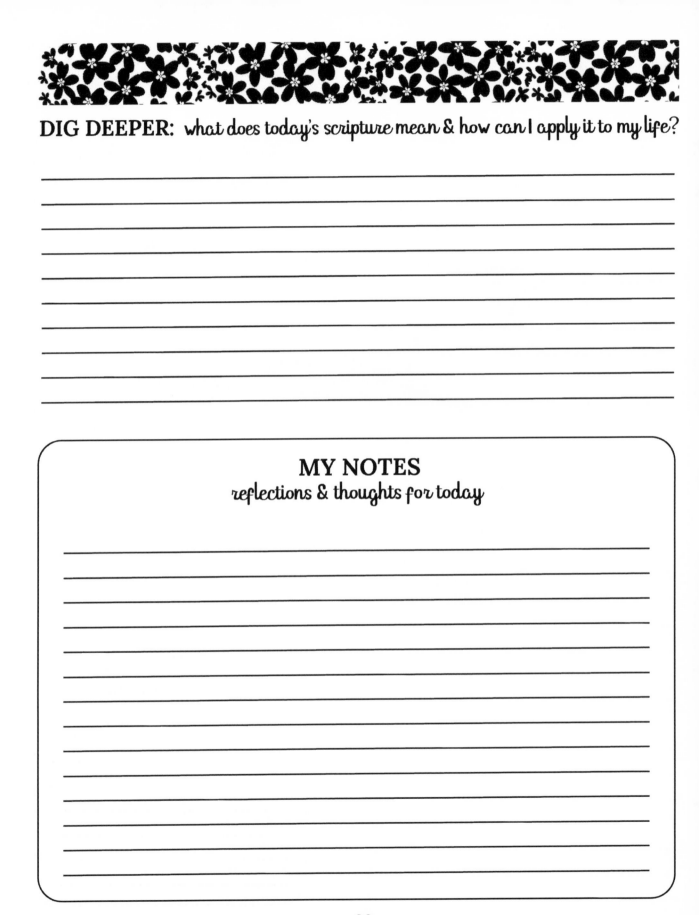

DIG DEEPER: what does today's scripture mean & how can I apply it to my life?

MY NOTES
reflections & thoughts for today

BIBLE READING
write it out & study the verses

make note of today's scripture reference:

PRAYER REQUESTS
& praise for answered prayers

GIVE THANKS
what I am thankful for today

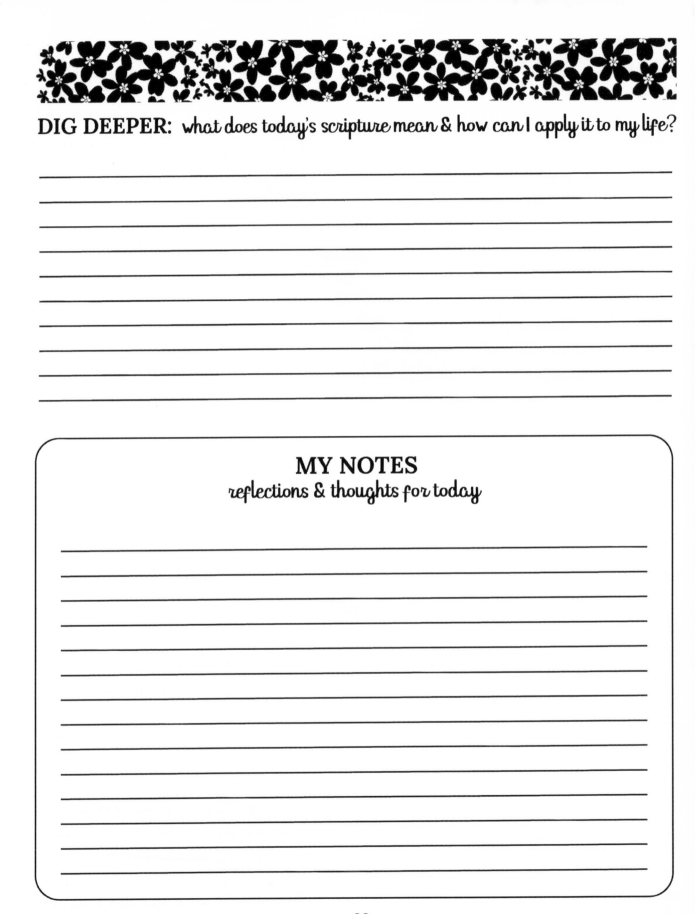

DIG DEEPER: *what does today's scripture mean & how can I apply it to my life?*

MY NOTES
reflections & thoughts for today

BIBLE READING
write it out & study the verses

make note of today's scripture reference:

PRAYER REQUESTS
& praise for answered prayers

GIVE THANKS
what I am thankful for today

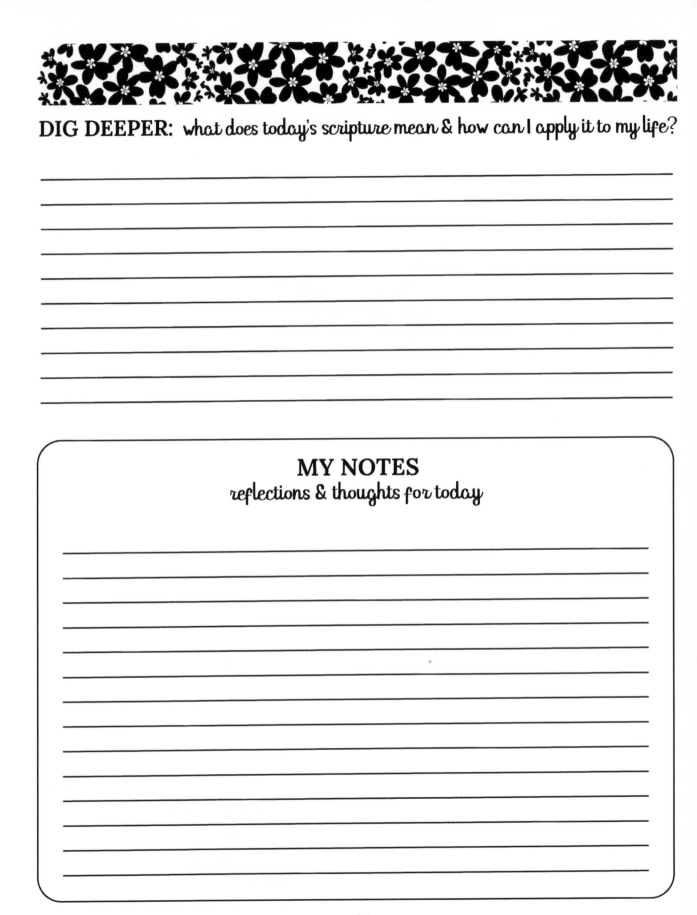

DIG DEEPER: what does today's scripture mean & how can I apply it to my life?

MY NOTES
reflections & thoughts for today

BIBLE READING
write it out & study the verses

make note of today's scripture reference:

PRAYER REQUESTS
& praise for answered prayers

GIVE THANKS
what I am thankful for today

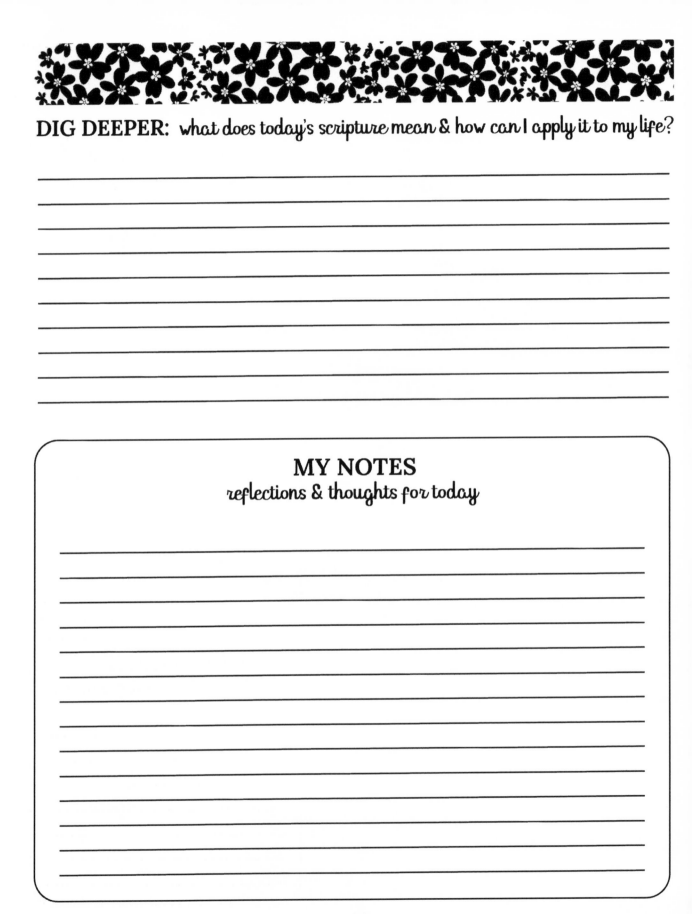

DIG DEEPER: what does today's scripture mean & how can I apply it to my life?

MY NOTES
reflections & thoughts for today

BIBLE READING
write it out & study the verses

make note of today's scripture reference:

PRAYER REQUESTS
& praise for answered prayers

GIVE THANKS
what I am thankful for today

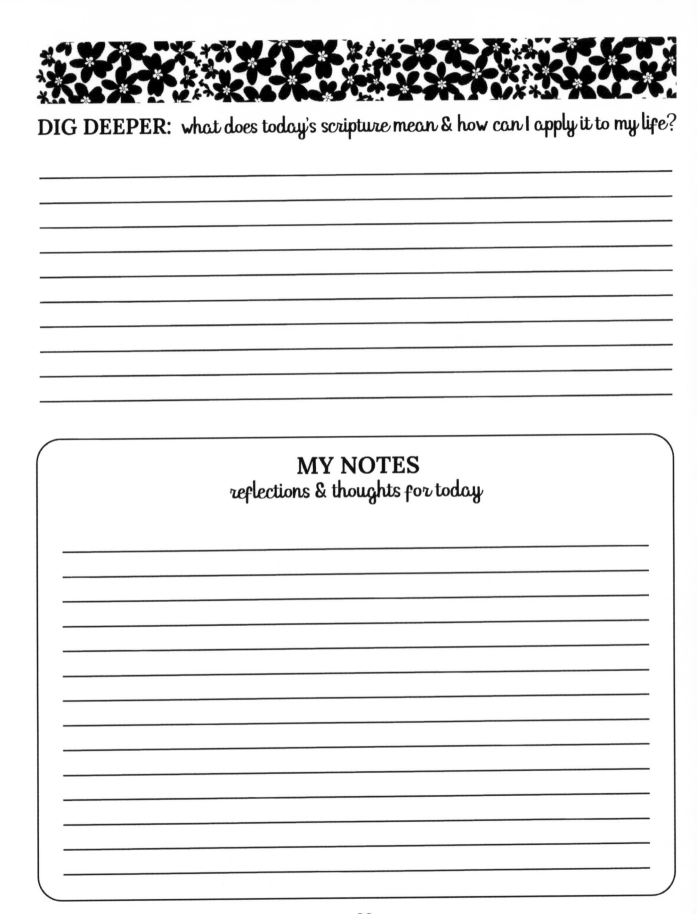

DIG DEEPER: *what does today's scripture mean & how can I apply it to my life?*

MY NOTES
reflections & thoughts for today

BIBLE READING
write it out & study the verses

make note of today's scripture reference:

PRAYER REQUESTS
& praise for answered prayers

GIVE THANKS
what I am thankful for today

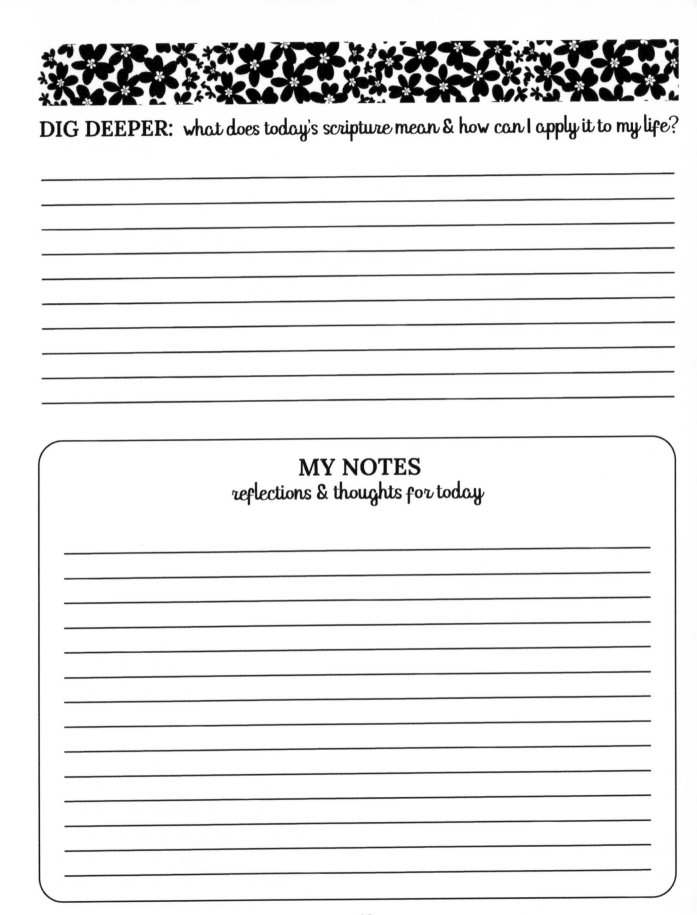

DIG DEEPER: *what does today's scripture mean & how can I apply it to my life?*

MY NOTES
reflections & thoughts for today

BIBLE READING
write it out & study the verses

make note of today's scripture reference:

PRAYER REQUESTS
& praise for answered prayers

GIVE THANKS
what I am thankful for today

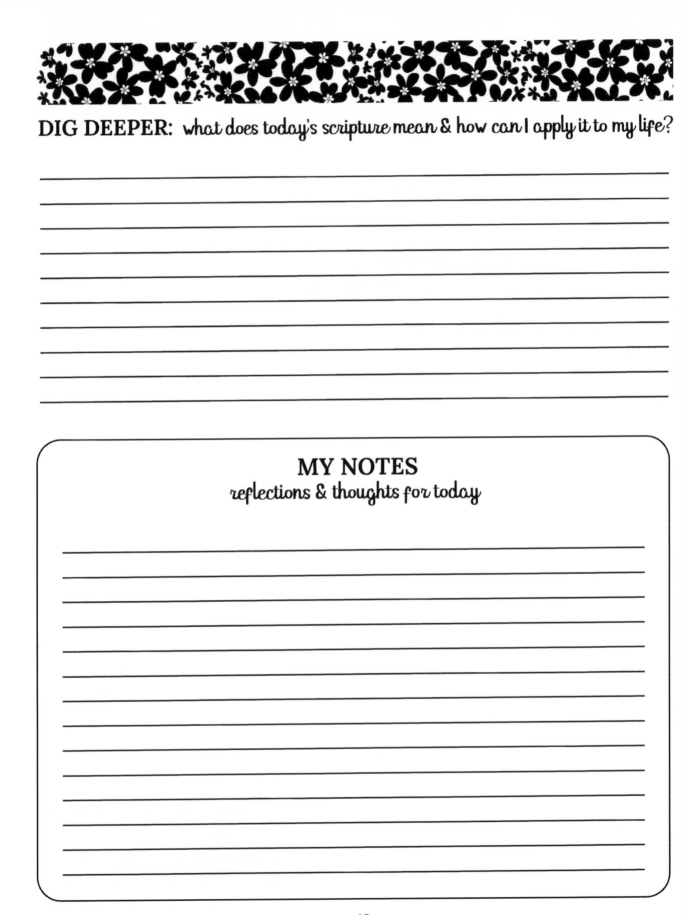

DIG DEEPER: *what does today's scripture mean & how can I apply it to my life?*

MY NOTES
reflections & thoughts for today

BIBLE READING
write it out & study the verses

make note of today's scripture reference:

PRAYER REQUESTS
& praise for answered prayers

GIVE THANKS
what I am thankful for today

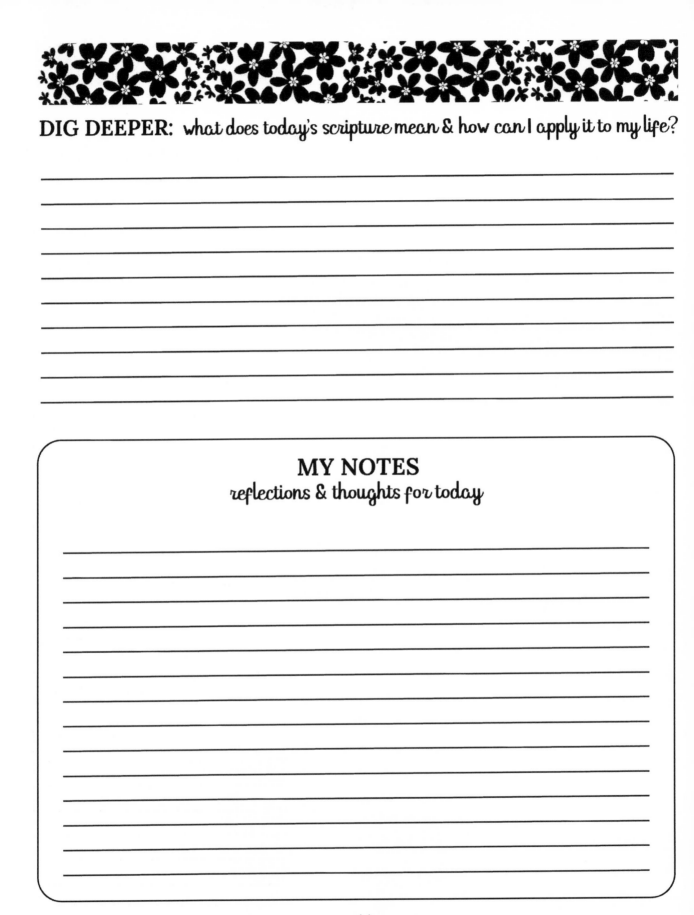

DIG DEEPER: what does today's scripture mean & how can I apply it to my life?

MY NOTES
reflections & thoughts for today

BIBLE READING
write it out & study the verses

make note of today's scripture reference:

PRAYER REQUESTS
& praise for answered prayers

GIVE THANKS
what I am thankful for today

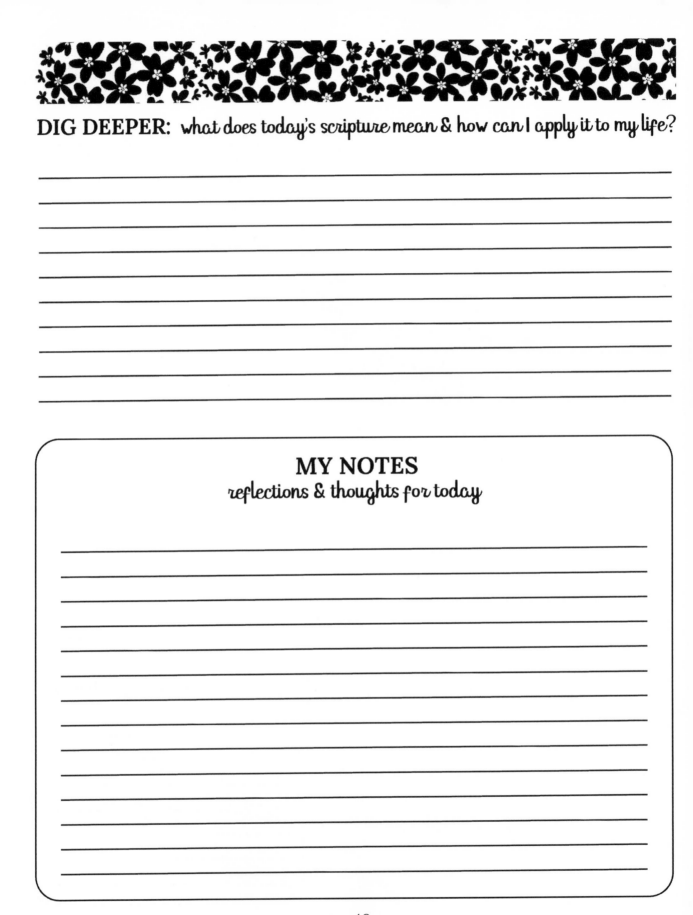

DIG DEEPER: what does today's scripture mean & how can I apply it to my life?

MY NOTES
reflections & thoughts for today

BIBLE READING
write it out & study the verses

make note of today's scripture reference:

PRAYER REQUESTS
& praise for answered prayers

GIVE THANKS
what I am thankful for today

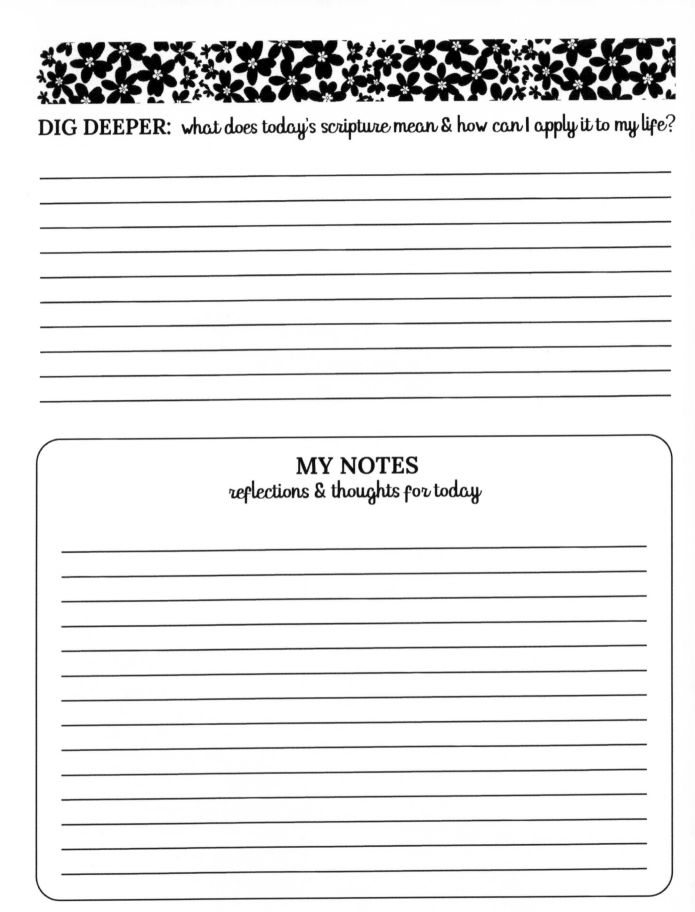

DIG DEEPER: what does today's scripture mean & how can I apply it to my life?

_____

_____

_____

_____

_____

_____

_____

_____

_____

_____

MY NOTES
reflections & thoughts for today

_____

_____

_____

_____

_____

_____

_____

_____

_____

_____

_____

date:_____

BIBLE READING
write it out & study the verses

make note of today's scripture reference:

PRAYER REQUESTS
& praise for answered prayers

GIVE THANKS
what I am thankful for today

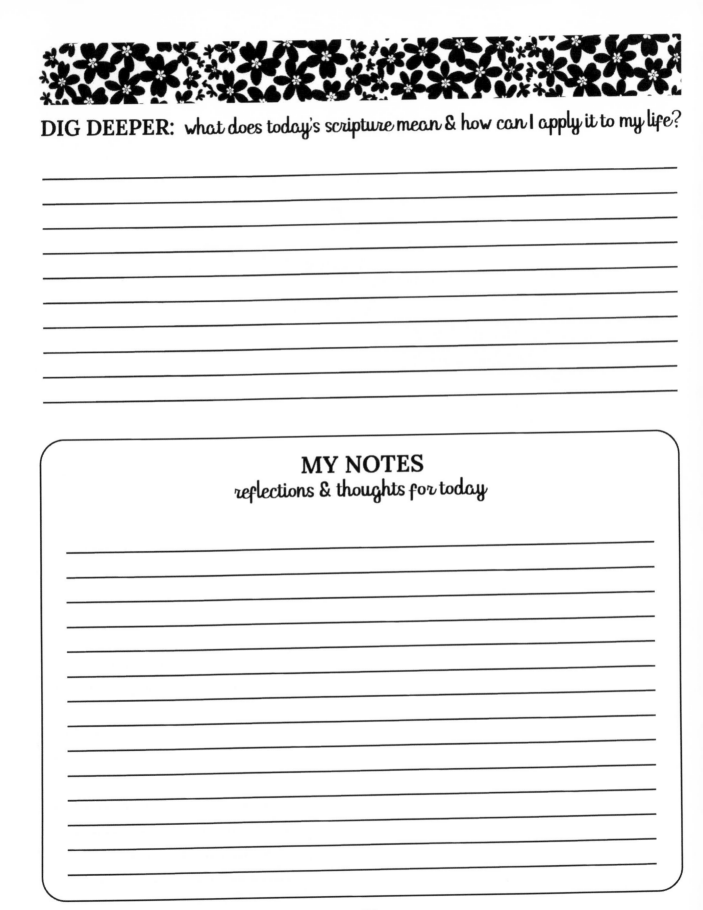

DIG DEEPER: *what does today's scripture mean & how can I apply it to my life?*

MY NOTES
reflections & thoughts for today

BIBLE READING
write it out & study the verses

make note of today's scripture reference:

PRAYER REQUESTS
& praise for answered prayers

GIVE THANKS
what I am thankful for today

DIG DEEPER: what does today's scripture mean & how can I apply it to my life?

MY NOTES
reflections & thoughts for today

BIBLE READING
write it out & study the verses

make note of today's scripture reference:

PRAYER REQUESTS
& praise for answered prayers

GIVE THANKS
what I am thankful for today

DIG DEEPER: what does today's scripture mean & how can I apply it to my life?

MY NOTES
reflections & thoughts for today

BIBLE READING
write it out & study the verses

make note of today's scripture reference:

_____

_____

_____

_____

_____

_____

_____

_____

_____

_____

_____

_____

_____

_____

_____

_____

_____

_____

PRAYER REQUESTS
& praise for answered prayers

_____

_____

_____

_____

_____

_____

_____

_____

_____

_____

_____

_____

_____

_____

GIVE THANKS
what I am thankful for today

_____

_____

_____

_____

_____

_____

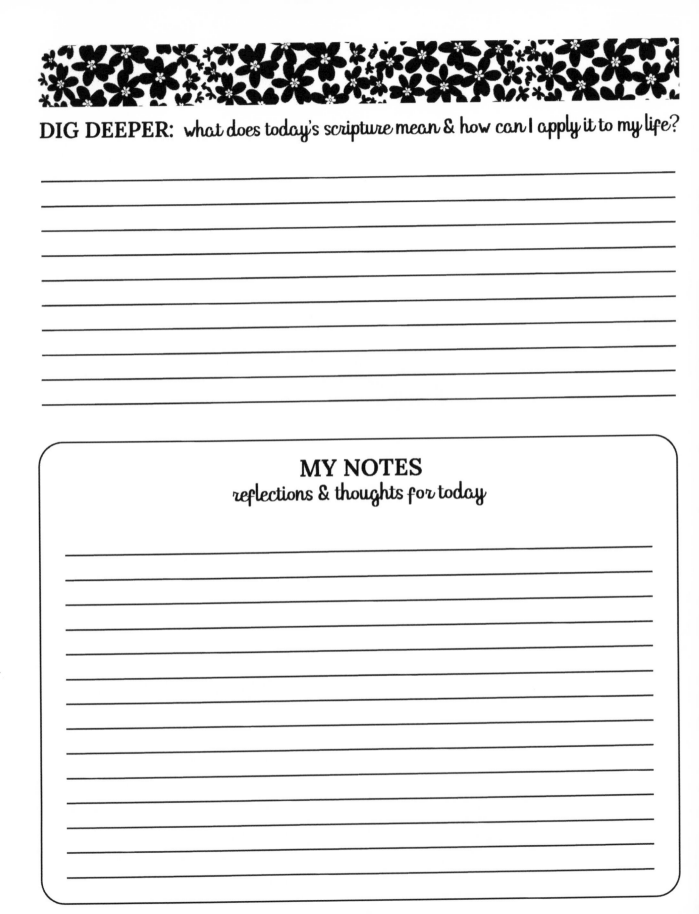

DIG DEEPER: *what does today's scripture mean & how can I apply it to my life?*

MY NOTES
reflections & thoughts for today

BIBLE READING
write it out & study the verses

make note of today's scripture reference:

PRAYER REQUESTS
& praise for answered prayers

GIVE THANKS
what I am thankful for today

DIG DEEPER: what does today's scripture mean & how can I apply it to my life?

MY NOTES
reflections & thoughts for today

BIBLE READING
write it out & study the verses

make note of today's scripture reference:

PRAYER REQUESTS
& praise for answered prayers

GIVE THANKS
what I am thankful for today

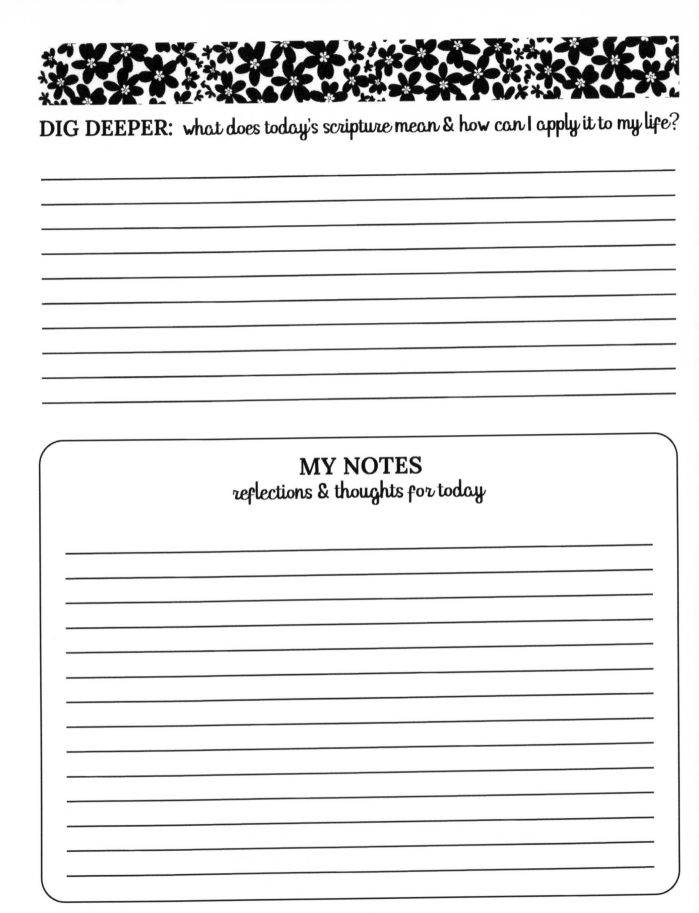

DIG DEEPER: *what does today's scripture mean & how can I apply it to my life?*

MY NOTES
reflections & thoughts for today

BIBLE READING
write it out & study the verses

make note of today's scripture reference:

PRAYER REQUESTS
& praise for answered prayers

GIVE THANKS
what I am thankful for today

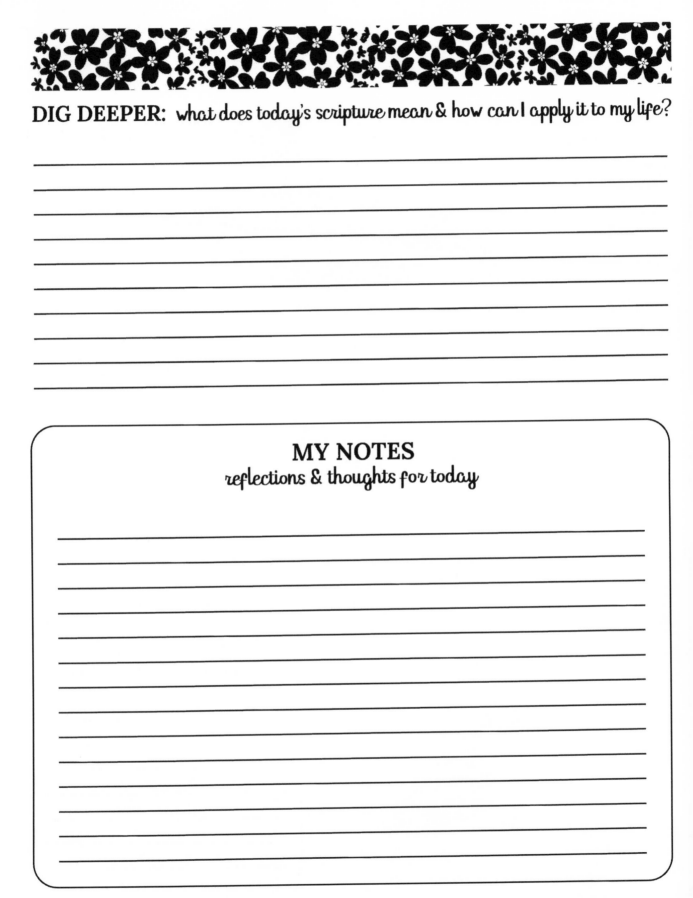

DIG DEEPER: what does today's scripture mean & how can I apply it to my life?

MY NOTES
reflections & thoughts for today

BIBLE READING
write it out & study the verses

make note of today's scripture reference:

PRAYER REQUESTS
& praise for answered prayers

GIVE THANKS
what I am thankful for today

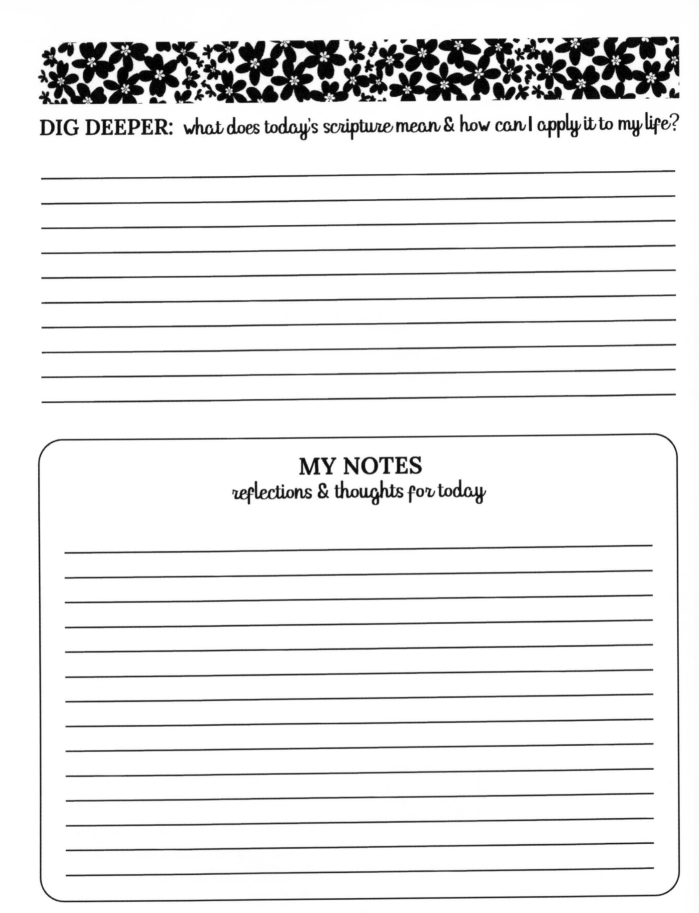

DIG DEEPER: what does today's scripture mean & how can I apply it to my life?

MY NOTES
reflections & thoughts for today

BIBLE READING
write it out & study the verses

make note of today's scripture reference:

PRAYER REQUESTS
& praise for answered prayers

GIVE THANKS
what I am thankful for today

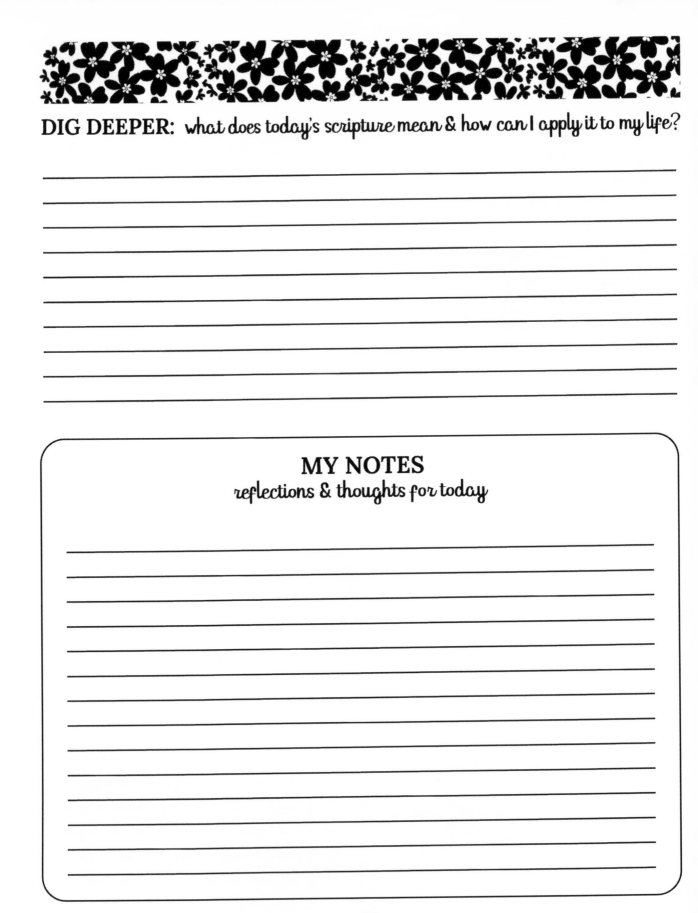

DIG DEEPER: *what does today's scripture mean & how can I apply it to my life?*

MY NOTES
reflections & thoughts for today

BIBLE READING
write it out & study the verses

make note of today's scripture reference:

PRAYER REQUESTS
& praise for answered prayers

GIVE THANKS
what I am thankful for today

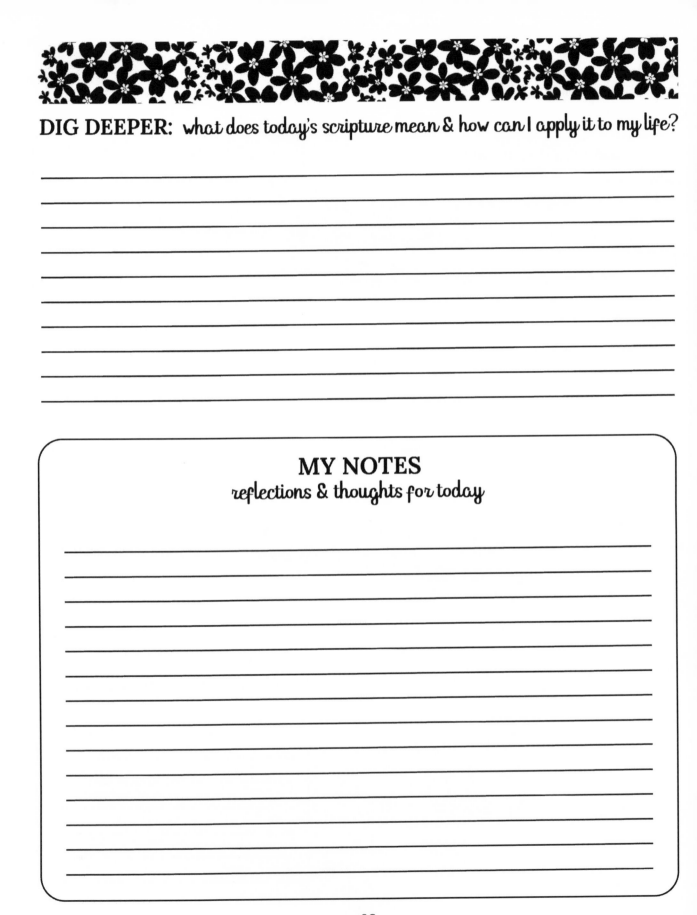

DIG DEEPER: *what does today's scripture mean & how can I apply it to my life?*

MY NOTES
reflections & thoughts for today

date:_____

BIBLE READING
write it out & study the verses

make note of today's scripture reference:

PRAYER REQUESTS
& praise for answered prayers

GIVE THANKS
what I am thankful for today

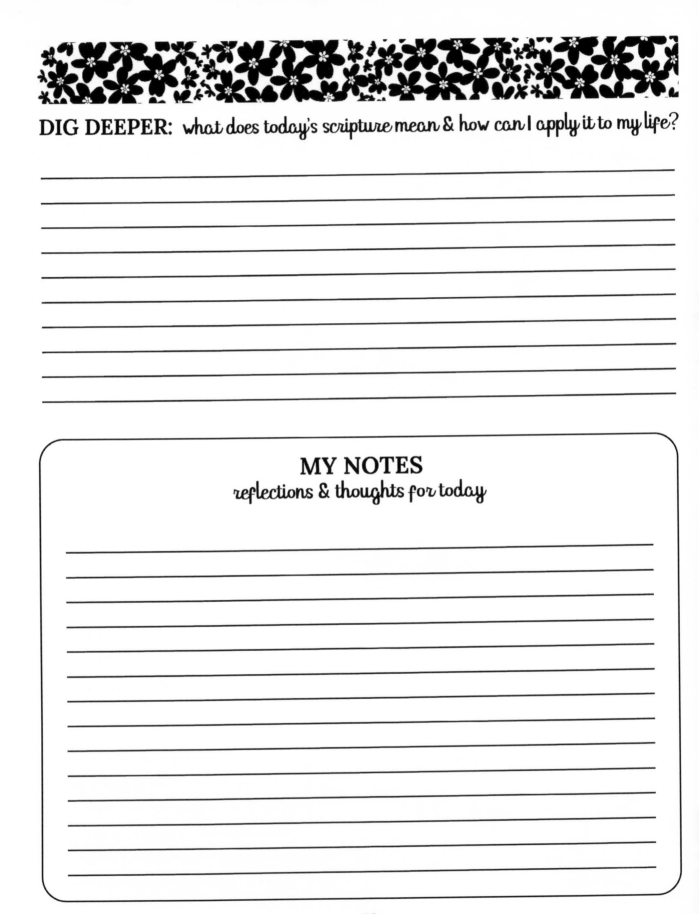

DIG DEEPER: what does today's scripture mean & how can I apply it to my life?

MY NOTES
reflections & thoughts for today

BIBLE READING
write it out & study the verses

make note of today's scripture reference:

PRAYER REQUESTS
& praise for answered prayers

GIVE THANKS
what I am thankful for today

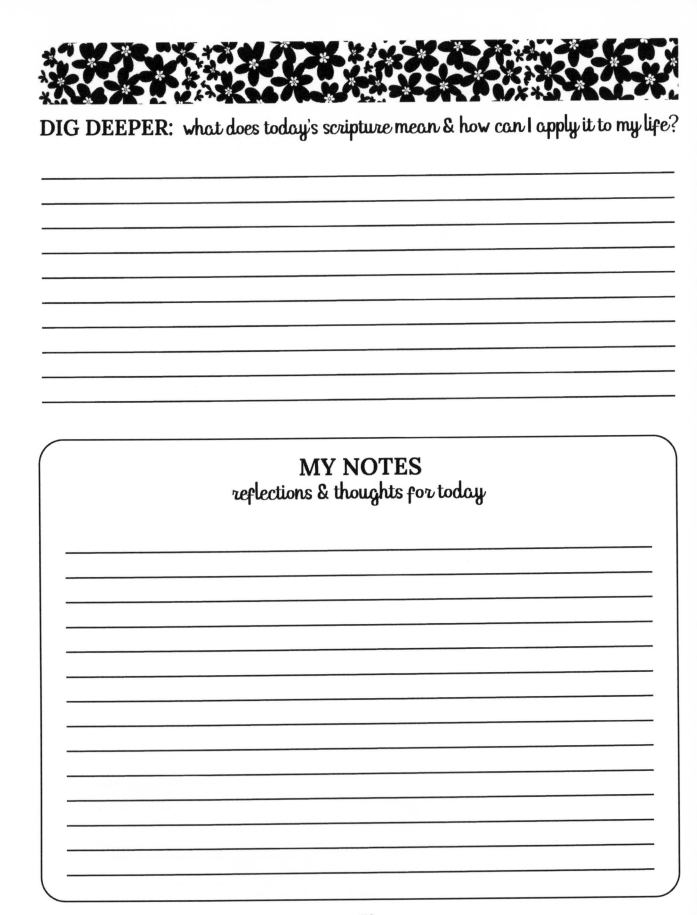

DIG DEEPER: *what does today's scripture mean & how can I apply it to my life?*

MY NOTES
reflections & thoughts for today

BIBLE READING
write it out & study the verses

make note of today's scripture reference:

PRAYER REQUESTS
& praise for answered prayers

GIVE THANKS
what I am thankful for today

DIG DEEPER: what does today's scripture mean & how can I apply it to my life?

MY NOTES
reflections & thoughts for today

BIBLE READING
write it out & study the verses

make note of today's scripture reference:

PRAYER REQUESTS
& praise for answered prayers

GIVE THANKS
what I am thankful for today

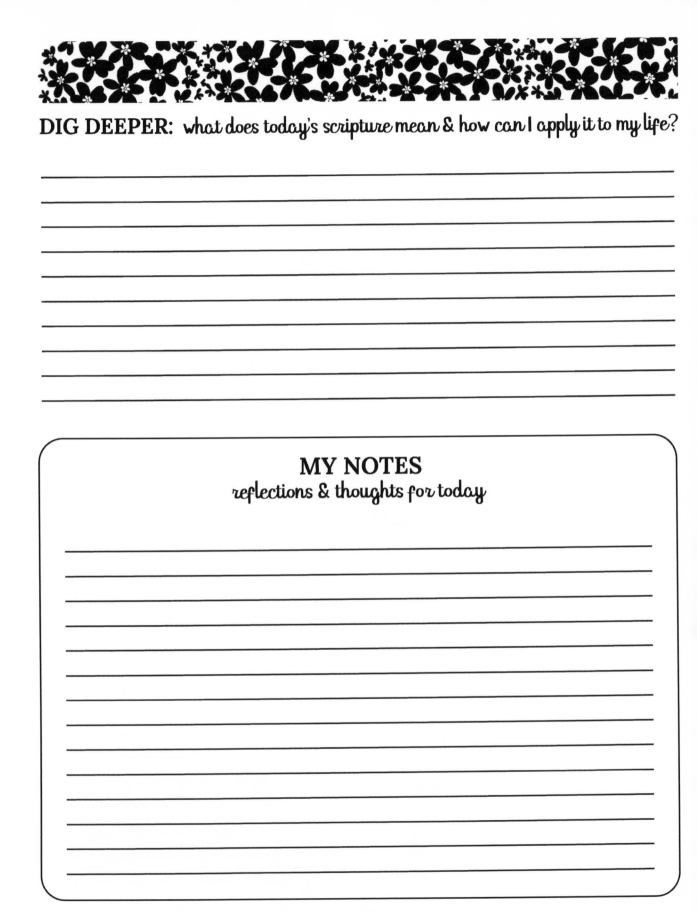

DIG DEEPER: what does today's scripture mean & how can I apply it to my life?

_____
_____
_____
_____
_____
_____
_____
_____
_____
_____

MY NOTES
reflections & thoughts for today

_____
_____
_____
_____
_____
_____
_____
_____
_____
_____
_____
_____

BIBLE READING
write it out & study the verses

make note of today's scripture reference:

PRAYER REQUESTS
& praise for answered prayers

GIVE THANKS
what I am thankful for today

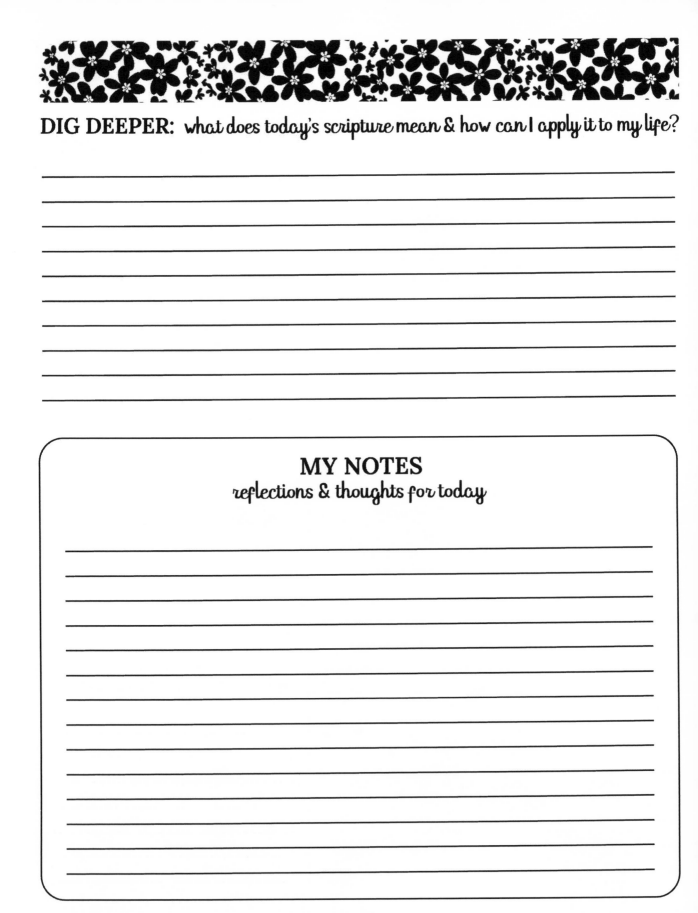

DIG DEEPER: what does today's scripture mean & how can I apply it to my life?

MY NOTES
reflections & thoughts for today

BIBLE READING
write it out & study the verses

make note of today's scripture reference:

PRAYER REQUESTS
& praise for answered prayers

GIVE THANKS
what I am thankful for today

DIG DEEPER: *what does today's scripture mean & how can I apply it to my life?*

_____

_____

_____

_____

_____

_____

_____

_____

_____

MY NOTES
reflections & thoughts for today

_____

_____

_____

_____

_____

_____

_____

_____

_____

_____

_____

BIBLE READING
write it out & study the verses

make note of today's scripture reference:

PRAYER REQUESTS
& praise for answered prayers

GIVE THANKS
what I am thankful for today

DIG DEEPER: what does today's scripture mean & how can I apply it to my life?

MY NOTES
reflections & thoughts for today

BIBLE READING
write it out & study the verses

make note of today's scripture reference:

PRAYER REQUESTS
& praise for answered prayers

GIVE THANKS
what I am thankful for today

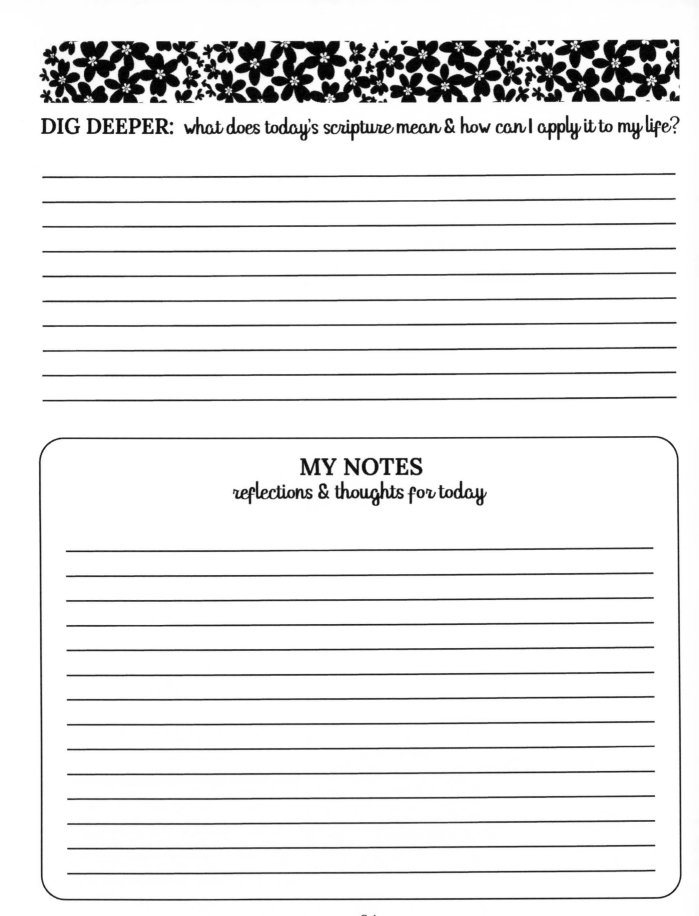

DIG DEEPER: what does today's scripture mean & how can I apply it to my life?

MY NOTES
reflections & thoughts for today

BIBLE READING
write it out & study the verses

make note of today's scripture reference:

PRAYER REQUESTS
& praise for answered prayers

GIVE THANKS
what I am thankful for today

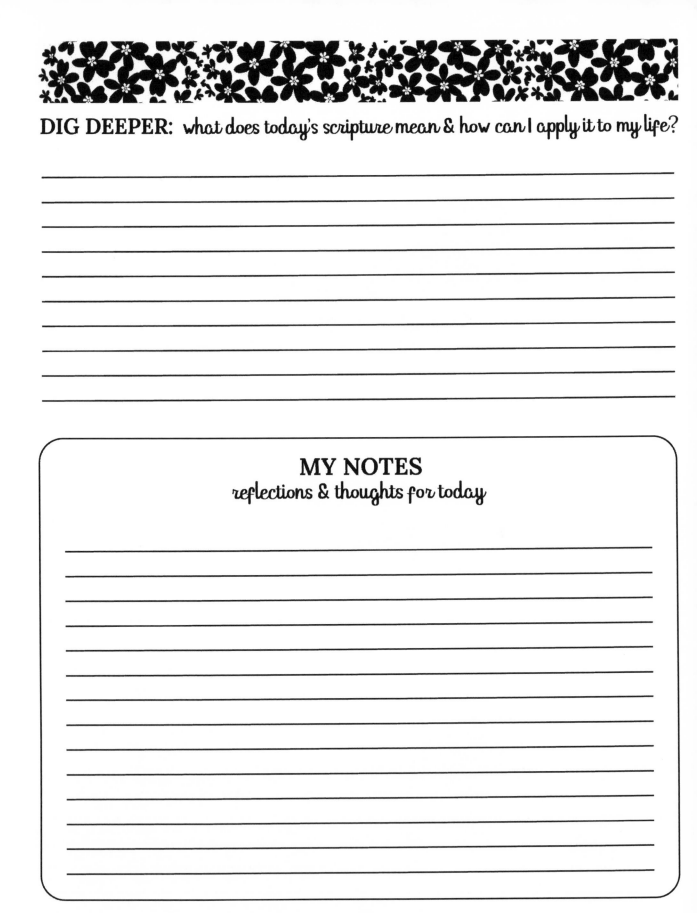

DIG DEEPER: what does today's scripture mean & how can I apply it to my life?

MY NOTES
reflections & thoughts for today

{ my additional notes & final reflections }

{ my additional notes & final reflections }

{ my additional notes & final reflections }

{ my additional notes & final reflections }

{ my additional notes & final reflections }

{ my additional notes & final reflections }

Made in the USA
Coppell, TX
11 February 2021